DESSY
SLEEPS DOWNSTAIRS

written by Neil Morris
illustrated by Geoffrey Butcher

Macdonald **345**

Chimpanzees live in the tropical forests of Africa.

A young chimpanzee called Dessy lives here with her mother and father.

All day long Dessy plays with her friends.
Their favourite game is hide and seek.

How many chimps are in the trees?
How many chimps are on the ground?
And how many are there altogether?

When it is time to sleep, Dessy's mother carries her off to bed.

She sleeps in a nest with her mother at the top of a tree. Father is just next door.

Early in the morning two friendly parrots
wake Dessy with a loud, cheerful squawk.

Which two parrots are the same size?
Which two chimps are the same size?

Which is the odd one out in each row?

One day Dessy's father finds a huge bunch
of bananas. There are enough for a feast.

So they drum on tree-trunks and hoot loudly
to tell their friends to come and join the party.

Can you help the chimp get to the banana?
Find a path with your finger.

They have a marvellous banana feast. Dessy
thinks her father was very clever to find them.

When they are full up the young chimps
have a game of chase.

But now the party is over and Dessy is
called up to bed.

How many parrots are there hidden in
the tree? Six

Dessy is so tired that she falls asleep down on the ground. But at night the forest is a dangerous place.

A lion is on the prowl nearby, hunting for food.

And a sly snake is slithering through the grass.

Which is the biggest snake?
Which is the biggest lion?
And which is the biggest parrot?

Find the shadow to go with each animal and fruit.

Dessy is fast asleep. She doesn't know that the dangerous animals are creeping nearer and nearer.

The clever parrots have seen the danger
and give a shrill warning squawk.

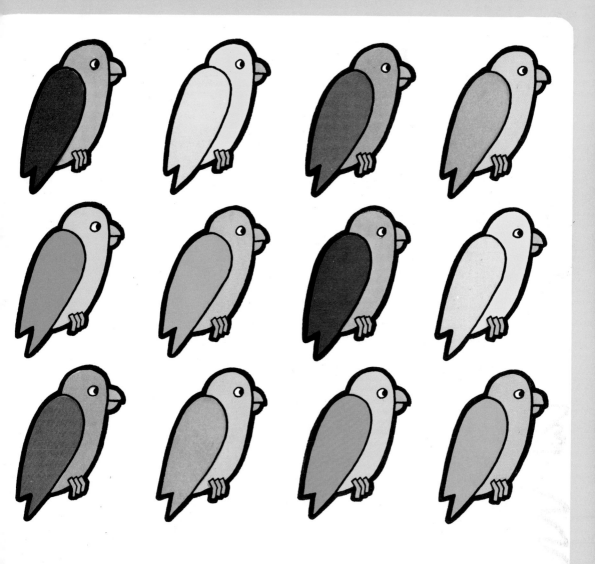

Find the pairs of parrots with the same colours.

Dessy scrambles up the tree to escape from the lion and the snake. Her mother lifts her into the nest.

Now that Dessy is safe and sound her mother and father make sure that the danger is past.

It's good to be home. Dessy never ever
wants to sleep downstairs again.